Let's Imagine...
A Dragon Is Discovered!

What if we discovered physical evidence that dragons existed? Explorers in a remote area of Romania uncovered the almost perfectly preserved frozen body of a centuries-dead Mountain Dragon. Located in a long-lost ice cave, the dragon's body was found along with its dead mother and several perished warriors. Evidence of a fiery battle between the men and the dragons was left behind for scientists to examine some **500** years later. With such a dramatic discovery, the legend of dragons would at last be revealed.

WHAT'S INSIDE

Myth or Legend

Myth, legend, or REAL?
Read on and decide.

Prehistoric Dragon

Sixty-five million years ago, this
dragon roamed the Earth with dinosaurs.

Marine Dragon

Marine Dragons coexisted with Prehistoric Dragons but when a giant meteor hit
the Earth, the Marine Dragons were the only members of the species to survive.

Forest Dragon

Forest Dragons were stealth predators but
mammals, not dragons, were their enemies.

Mountain Dragon

Mountain Dragons were the last of this
mythical species. Man wiped them out by learning the mysteries
of the dragons' most lethal defense: fire.

Making It Real

How did this story come to be? Were they real?
Discover the technological secrets scientists and animation
experts used to make their case.

An Ancient Worldwide Legend...Or Fantasy?

Should we believe in dragons? Throughout time nearly every culture has recorded the existence of a magnificent, fire-breathing, flying beast. Are dragons fantasy or reality? How can we believe that they are real when so much scientific evidence says dragons couldn't have existed? But what if these fantastic stories were more than myth? Stories and myths about dragons come from the high seas, from Greenland, from Europe, from the Far East, from all over the world...from cultures that could never have communicated and who lived in vastly different time periods. How? Perhaps, somehow, the stories were **REAL**. Turn the pages as we explore the what-ifs, the maybes, the possibilities of dragons.

What Might Have Happened To Prehistoric Dragons?

Some **65** million years ago, a meteorite bigger than the tallest mountain you've ever seen slammed into the earth and killed off the dragon population—and most other creatures that roamed the earth—except those that lived in the sea. This explosion was called the **K-T Event.**

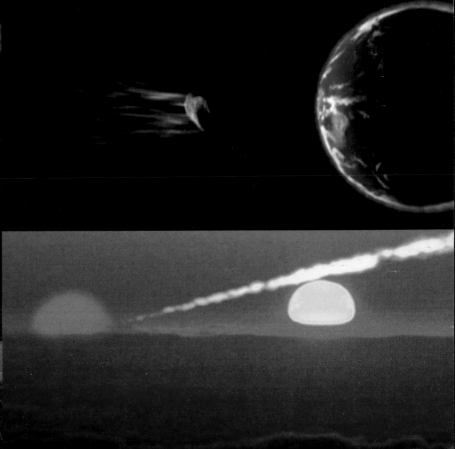

How Would Dragons Fly?

Right: Scientists autopsy the remains of a dragon found in an ice cave.

Below: A scientist removes the flight bladder from the recovered body of the Mountain Dragon.

The flight bladders.

For years scientists have tried to learn how dragons could have flown. Some scientists have a theory: These flight bladders (above and left) were one of the essential secrets to dragons' ability to fly. All animals have bacteria in their gut that helps digest food. A byproduct of the bacteria and food is gas, which is released into the atmosphere. Not so for dragons; their gas didn't go to waste. It was channeled into these flight bladders. The gas was predominately made up of hydrogen, which is 14 times less dense than air. Think of a balloon. You put hydrogen in a balloon and it floats. Same concept for a dragon.

Fire Breathing

Above: Scientists examine the teeth of the recovered body of the Mountain Dragon. Dragons not only had incisors for ripping meat from their kills but they also had molars—strange for a meat-eating predator. The scientists discovered that the molars were used for grinding platinum, found in nearly every dragon's territory. The platinum was used to ignite the hydrogen found in the dragons' flight bladders, which was key in their ability to breathe fire. But how did this remarkable ability not burn their throats? Similar to crocodiles' false palate at the back of their throats to keep water from entering their lungs, dragons had a false palate to prevent fire from entering and igniting their bodies. The fleshy valves served as a prevention for a

Dragons could have come in all shapes and sizes. If dragons had existed, these are the most likely to have evolved.

Prehistoric Dragons were the largest flying animals to ever have lived. They thrived as they managed to coexist with—and many times battle—the dinosaurs. So what brought an end to the era of the Prehistoric Dragon?

At the peak of these creatures' success, a meteorite the size of Mount Everest smashed into the planet. Known as the **K-T Event**, it wiped out nearly all life on land—but somehow the species survived, because most life in the sea—including the Prehistoric Dragons' cousin, the Marine Dragon—avoided extinction.

Not yet having learned to fly, a young Prehistoric Dragon attempts to defend itself against the most fierce predator to ever walk the earth—Tyrannosaurus Rex—by extending its wings to give the illusion that it is much larger than it really is. Not deterred by this bluff, the T-Rex remains in attack mode. Next the young dragon attempts to protect itself by producing a piercing scream that carries for miles. Even this incredibly painful screech does not get the T-Rex to back off but the dragon's mother hears it and comes to her son's rescue.

Fooling T-Rex

A Dragon Protects Her Young From T-Rex

n an attempt to protect her young, a Prehistoric mother Dragon breathes a stream of blazing fire at a Tyrannosaurus Rex who is invading her territory. The T-Rex will not last the night after being hit with the igniting blaze, but the mother is also fatally injured when T-Rex rips apart her wing. With the broken wing, she can no longer fly to hunt for food for herself and her offspring. To survive her son must do what takes years for dragons to do—learn to fly.

Dragons Fight For Territory

A young Prehistoric male Dragon, right, prepares to take on an Alpha male dragon, left, in the fight of his life to win the older dragon's territory. With territory comes a guaranteed supply of food and a mate. If the young male has any chance of winning this duel, he must be at his very best. To prepare, he must have plenty of fuel in his body to produce fire. To ignite that fire, he must have a catalyst—platinum. He uses his grinding molars to take on stores of this very valuable and rare mineral found at the heart of every dragon territory. The platinum ignites the fuel—hydrogen and methane gases—stored in the flight bladder-caused by bacteria—and the exploding chemicals have nowhere to go but out. Pow. Fire! After a fierce battle, the young dragon prevails, and the territory and all its treasures become his.

When a meteorite slammed into the Earth some **65** million years ago, it wiped out all life on land larger than a cat. But somehow dragons survived. How?

Those species that did survive the **K-T Event** were all aquatic. The survivors included sharks, turtles, crocodiles, and the cousin of the Prehistoric Dragon—the Marine Dragon. Essentially, Marine Dragons swam from extinction. Over time, their flight bladders had become swim bladders, their large wings shrank to become fins, and their powerful tails became rudders. Marine Dragons thrived. Then, as global temperatures rose and the land recovered from the **K-T Event**, some Marine Dragons returned to shallow waters. Through streams and rivers, they eventually took their first tentative steps onto land and into forests.

Dragon

How to remove your posters.

A parent can gently bend the staples up and remove all four posters at once. Be sure to ask a parent because the staples are very sharp! Remember to fold the staples back down once the posters are out.

medieval times, it was restricted largely to
ume is, however, slightly inappropriate since the
nd forests and was not restricted to mountains
human population restricted its habitat.
agons had six limbs (a pair of wings in
lvantageous developmental mutation that
two-winged **Prehistoric Dragon.**
t compared with that of the **Marine Dragon;**
ere a long, flexible vertebral column is a
as the body, ending in a razor-sharp
a defensive weapon. **A sideswipe from a**

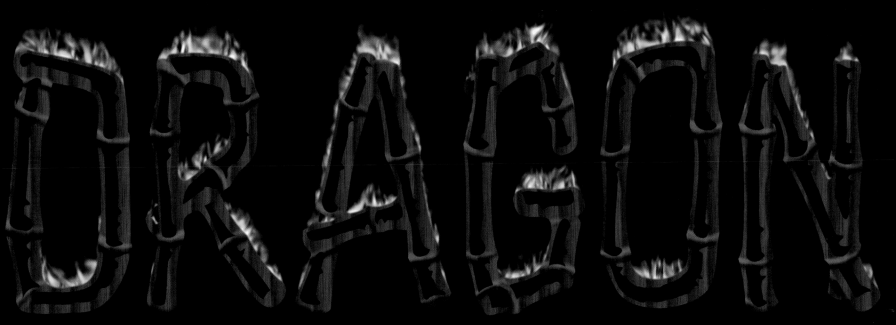

gons that came back on land. **Dinosaurs were gone**

the void—mammals. **And mammals provided**

ch them. **The Forest Dragons had long, slender**

s expected of a water creature, but is it suited for

n, yes. **Flight bladders became a valuable tool for**

all for powered flight, but they were capable of

tors with remarkable camouflage that rendered

became easy. **The dragons could more easily digest**

ecame a culinary tool. **This fire was the key that**

ut soon they had to face humans, who understood

dragons' most powerful weapon against them.

When a meteorite slammed into the Earth some 65 million years ago, it wiped out all life on land larger than a cat. But somehow dragons survived. How? Those species that did survive the **K-T Event** were all aquatic. The survivors included sharks, turtles, crocodiles, and the cousin of the Prehistoric Dragon— the Marine Dragon. Essentially, Marine Dragons swam from extinction. Over time, their flight bladders had become swim bladders, their large wings shrank to become fins, and their powerful tails became rudders. Marine Dragons thrived. Then, as global temperatures rose and the land recovered from the **K-T** Event, some Marine Dragons returned to shallow waters. Through streams and rivers, they eventually took their first tentative steps onto land and into forests.

IC DRAGON

shapes and sizes. **If dragons had
 to have evolved. Prehistoric
g animals to ever have lived. They
ith—and many times battle—the
 the era of the Prehistoric Dragon?
s, a meteorite the size of Mount
wn as the K-T Event, it wiped out
 the species survived, because most
oric Dragons' cousin, the Marine**

PREHISTOR

Dragons could have come in all
existed, these are the most lik
Dragons were the largest fly
thrived as they managed to coexist
dinosaurs. So what brought an end
At the peak of these creatures' succ
Everest smashed into the planet. K
nearly all life on land—but somehow
life in the sea—including the Prehi
Dragon—avoided extinction.

FOREST

Forest Dragons evolved from the first Marine D[...]
and a new order of animals had risen up to f[...]
plentiful food for the dragons—if they could [...]
bodies and walked close to the ground. This physiqu[...]
one that lived in a bamboo forest? With some adapta[...]
the Forest Dragon. These dragons' wings were too [...]
gliding over short distances. They were stealthy pr[...]
them nearly invisible. Catching prey—like forest pig[...]
cooked meat so the ancient weapon of breathing fir[...]
helped these creatures survive the Age of Mammals[...]
the possibilities and uses of fire, and humans used t[...]

Mountain

The **Mountain Dragon** is so called because
mountains and other remote habitats. The
species was much more widespread in low
before the pressures of agriculture and a growi

Like all post-Cretaceous dragons, Mountain
addition to two pairs of legs), the result of an
occurred after the extinction of the two-legge

The **Mountain Dragon's** body was relatively s
however, a shorter body is essential for flight,
disadvantage. The tail was approximately as lo
arrowhead-shaped structure that could be used
dragon's tail could easily sever a person's arm.

MARINE
DRAGON

FOREST

Forest Dragons evolved from the first **Marine Dragons** that came back on land. Dinosaurs were gone and a new order of animals had risen up to fill the void—mammals. And mammals provided plentiful food for the dragons—if they could catch them. The Forest Dragons had long, slender bodies and walked close to the ground. This physique is expected of a water creature, but is it suited for one that lived in a bamboo forest? With some adaptation, yes. Flight bladders became a valuable tool for the Forest Dragon. These dragons' wings were too small for powered flight, but they were capable of gliding over short distances. They were stealthy

DRAGON

predators with remarkable camouflage that rendered them nearly invisible. Catching prey—like forest pigs—became easy. The dragons could more easily digest cooked meat so the ancient weapon of breathing fire became a culinary tool. This fire was the key that helped these creatures survive the Age of Mammals. But soon they had to face humans, who understood the possibilities and uses of fire, and humans used the dragons' most powerful weapon against them.

Mountain

Dragon

The Mountain Dragon is so called because in medieval times, it was restricted largely to mountains and other remote habitats. The name is, however, slightly inappropriate since the species was much more widespread in lowland forests and was not restricted to mountains before the pressures of agriculture and a growing human population restricted its habitat.

Like all post-Cretaceous dragons, Mountain Dragons had six limbs (a pair of wings in addition to two pairs of legs), the result of an advantageous developmental mutation that occurred after the extinction of the two-legged, two-winged Prehistoric Dragon.

The Mountain Dragon's body was relatively short compared with that of the Marine Dragon; however, a shorter body is essential for flight, where a long, flexible vertebral column is a disadvantage. The tail was approximately as long as the body, ending in a razor-sharp arrowhead-shaped structure that could be used as a defensive weapon. A sideswipe from a dragon's tail could easily sever a person's arm.

Dragon Courtship

Dragons had their own way of dating and their courtship was a fantastic sight. In an age-old aerial display, a female dragon led her prospective mate in a ritual—the first date. In a dazzling acrobatic display, the dragons sailed and twisted through the air. They flirted, determining if they would be compatible to start a family.

Dragon Eggs

Mother dragons were extremely protective of their young. Above, a mother dragon breathes fire onto her eggs, which she has enclosed in a uniquely formed rock configuration, to keep them from becoming too cold and killing them before they can hatch.

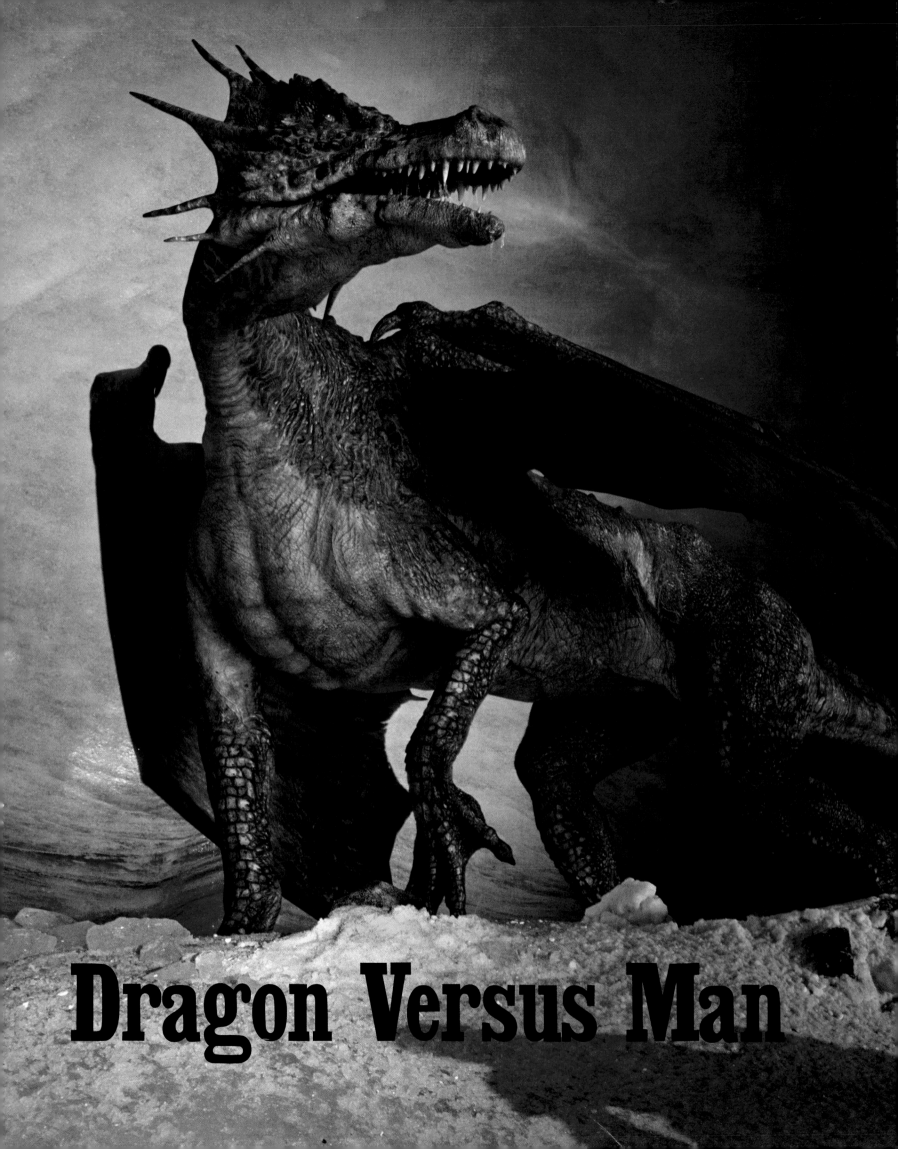

Dragon Versus Man

Mountain Dragons sometimes used ice caves as their lairs. That was where the females laid their eggs and watched them carefully during their 30-day incubation period. Temperature control was essential for the survival of the dragon embryos—too-hot or too-cold temperatures would kill them. Females became very aggressive and suspicious of any creature who approached their nest, even their mate. This dragon laid two eggs but only one survived—a daughter. And this was, perhaps, the last dragon to ever be born. Food sources were scarce and because the male dragon does not help rear its young, the mother was forced to find an easier supply of food so she could stay close to her daughter. She began to prey on the livestock of local farms, making herself a criminal in the eyes of man. This cave soon became a brutal crime scene. A local lord and his squire were determined to put a stop to the raids on their livestock. While the mother was out hunting for the now very scarce food, her daughter was killed by these men. The mother's fate is soon sealed as men returned to find her in the cave, weak from no food, which meant no fuel to create fire. She was trapped. The battle began and man prevailed again. But not without a fight. The bloody crime scene was soon frozen in time for a future generation to uncover.

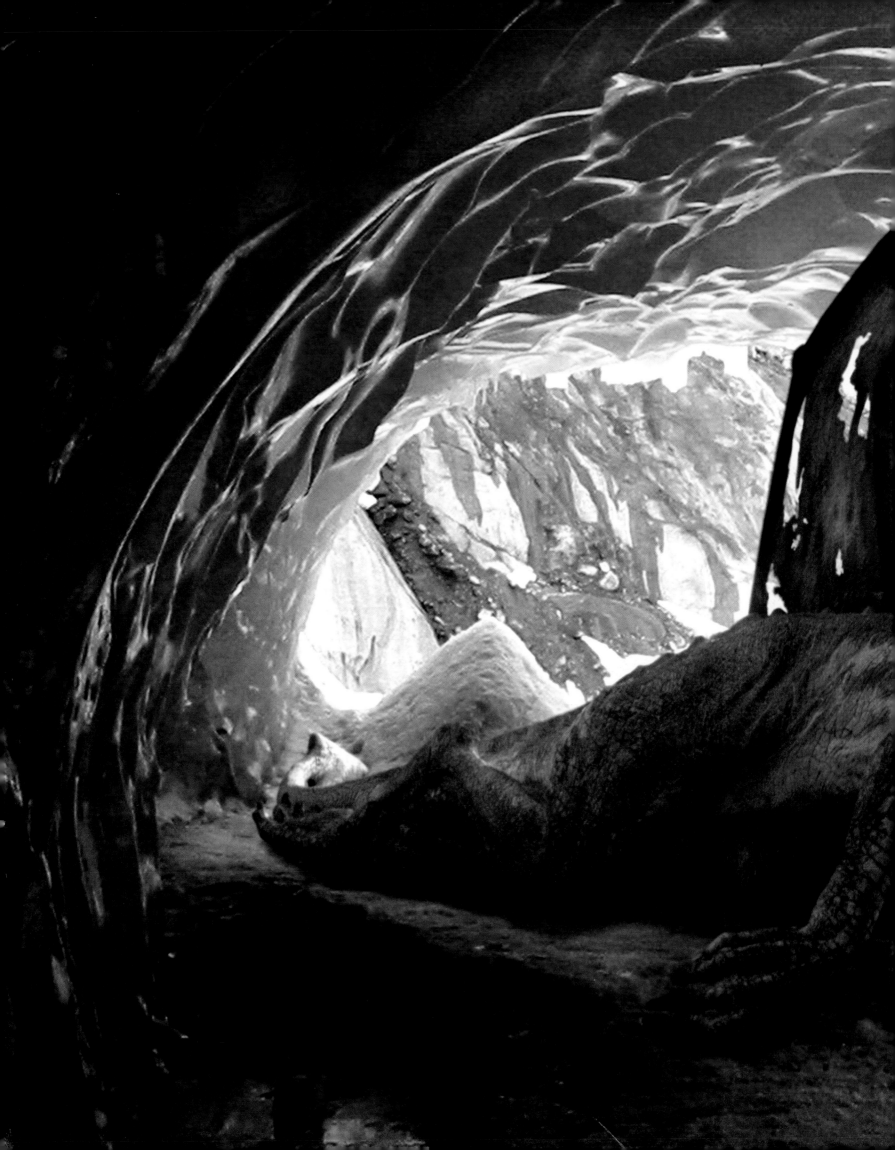

The Last Dragon

The slain dragon lies in her final resting place after putting up a fierce fight against the species' final and most deadly enemy—humans.

MAKING

IT REAL

All the dragons in the show "Dragons: A Fantasy Made Real," the basis for this book, were created by using computers much like the one you have at home. None of the dragons are real, but computers were used to make them seem that way.

There are several steps to making the dragons come to life. First, many sketches are made by artists to decide just how each dragon will look. Then the drawings are used to make clay model sculptures, called maquettes, of each animal by people who decide all the final details of the dragons. These models are about 2 feet long and show just how the final dragon will look, right down to the shape of the eyes

After the sculptures are finished, all the details are put into a computer using 3-D scanners, which are machines that take special pictures of the sculpture to help the computer see it in three dimensions. The computer now has a picture of the dragon that can be turned, flipped over, and looked at from top and bottom.

The first stage of the dragon is to turn it into a "wireframe model" just like the one you see on the right side of this picture. It is made up of thousands of different-shaped and -sized rectangles, called polygons, that are used to make the shape and surfaces of the dragon. Each

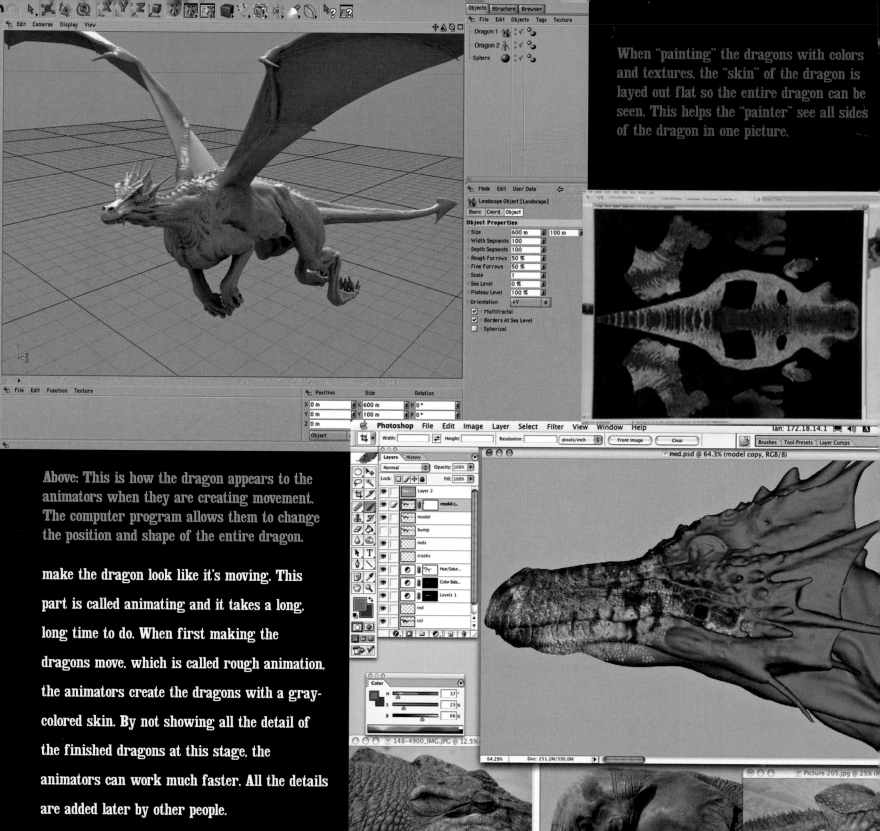

When "painting" the dragons with colors and textures, the "skin" of the dragon is layed out flat so the entire dragon can be seen. This helps the "painter" see all sides of the dragon in one picture.

Above: This is how the dragon appears to the animators when they are creating movement. The computer program allows them to change the position and shape of the entire dragon.

make the dragon look like it's moving. This part is called animating and it takes a long, long time to do. When first making the dragons move, which is called rough animation, the animators create the dragons with a gray-colored skin. By not showing all the detail of the finished dragons at this stage, the animators can work much faster. All the details are added later by other people.

Every step the dragon takes might mean the animator must move hundreds of polygons thousands of times! It might take a week for the animator to make a dragon take just a few steps.

After all the rough animation is done, another person "paints" all the skin textures and skin colors onto the dragons. The person who does this work uses animals from real life to get ideas for colors, patterns, and skin types. Alligator, elephant, and rhino skins

Above: By using pictures of real animals for ideas, the dragons were "painted" with patterns and skin textures. Each dragon had its own pattern of spots and markings and skin color.

were used by the "painters" to copy in order to help them make the dragons look realistic.

After the textures are added to the rough animation, another person helps create the lighting, shadows, smoke, water, and the

Above: This is an example of "rough animation" showing how the T-Rex and the mother dragon fought one another. The bottom picture shows how the final picture looked in the show.

cool things that help the dragons look so real. This is when fire breathing is added to the animation. Sometimes the fire was photographed from a real fire and added to the animated dragons while other fire was computer-generated.

Do you remember the dragons flying through the clouds and around mountains? Almost all of the backgrounds, or settings, you saw were from real places on Earth. Planes and helicopters were used to fly cameras up and over mountains for the scenes of dragons flying. Other backgrounds were filmed in other places, sometimes in the jungle or even under water. All of these

scenes used in Dragons are called "plates" or "backplates," and dragons are added to them after they've been animated.

The last step of animating is to put all the parts together. The fully animated dragon is combined with the lighting, effects, and the backplates and they are "composited" or put together into one big picture. Now the dragons look just like they appeared on screen. It took the animators months to fully animate all the dragons in the program and composite them into the final program "Dragons: A Fantasy Made Real."